Making Good Sense
of the Bible Together

Foreword by
Paula Gooder

Bible Society
Stonehill Green
Westlea
Swindon SN5 7DG
biblesociety.org.uk

First published 2015 by The British and Foreign Bible Society.

ISBN: 978-0-564-04427-6

Production by Bible Society Resources Ltd, a wholly-owned
subsidiary of The British and Foreign Bible Society
Cover and text design by Colin Hall, TypeFunction

Printed in Great Britain
BSRL/2M/2015

Contents

Foreword

We all know that reading the Bible is important. It is the Word of God. It can speak to our hearts and transform our lives. By reading it we can learn more of God and of his love for the world. But if we are honest, reading the Bible is not always easy. It is so big. It has so many different kinds of writing in it. Some passages appear to be very confusing and difficult to understand. So what do we do when we hit problems and don't understand how to go on?

Making Good Sense of the Bible Together is designed to introduce you to some of the questions you need to ask in order to get to know the Bible more deeply. Learning to ask these questions about what lies behind the text (history), about what the text is like (literature) and about what we bring to our reading of the text (us) are tried and tested methods for understanding the Bible. This course will introduce you to the kinds of questions you need to ask in order to go deeper in your knowledge and understanding of the Bible.

The methods of reading the Bible you will meet in this course do not in any way replace the need for the Holy Spirit's insight as we read. As Paul says in 1 Corinthians 14.15 we pray and praise with the Spirit and with the mind, not either/or. This course introduces you to some of the questions, issues and topics that your mind needs for a deeper knowledge of the Bible. It will of course be empty, however, without the guidance of the Holy Spirit.

One of the emphases of this course is on reading the Bible together. This is one of the most important things you can do. As the Ethiopian eunuch discovered in Acts 8.27-39, we need the help of other Christians as we read the Bible to give us insight and new inspiration. Possibly more important than any of the skills referred to in this course is the importance of reading together, of asking, together, what God's word is saying and of allowing it to change us as we read.

Learning to make good sense of the Bible is a lifetime's work. A six-week course cannot hope to teach you everything you need know for reading the Bible well, but it can begin to introduce you to a few of the questions you need to ask so that you can go deeper and deeper in your reading of the Bible. Learning to make good sense of the Bible is an adventure. May God bless you as you continue your quest to know more of him and to hear his voice speaking more clearly in your life.

Dr Paula Gooder
Theologian in Residence, Bible Society

Introduction to the course

Welcome

Welcome to *Making Good Sense of the Bible Together*. Over the next six sessions you will explore some of the key aspects to understanding and interpreting the Bible well. You will like some better than others. Some will seem more important to you than others. Some you will agree with, others you won't. At the end of these six sessions, though, we hope that your vision of the Bible will be bigger and broader. We hope that your minds will be stretched and your hearts warmed, but most importantly that you will open the Bible with even greater enthusiasm to make good sense of the word of God.

The Bible remains the bestselling book of all time – over 6 billion copies of the Bible have been printed to date! It has influenced countless works of literature, music and art. It has shaped the laws and politics of many western countries and continues to inspire a growing number of Christians around the globe. This is because through the words of the Bible, God speaks to change and transform our lives. As a result it is important for us to do everything that we can to understand the Bible and what it is saying. This course seeks to provide some of the tools that you will need for this as well as the space for you to ask questions about how you might understand the Bible better.

You may be concerned that in-depth study of the Bible could undermine your faith, or suck the life out of your relationship with God. If this is your fear, be reassured. The intention of this course is to enhance faith by offering a deeper, richer, more vibrant insight into the Bible. The more important something is – and you don't get much more important than reading the Bible well – the more important it is to approach it as well as you can. Part of what you will gain from the course is the experience of reading the Bible as a group. Many through the ages have discovered this stretches minds and hearts and opens up new ways of thinking. As you progress through the course, however, continue reading the Bible on your own, listening to God speak to you through it about how to live your life. You will hopefully grow in confidence that you are hearing the message clearly through what you are learning.

The majority of examples used in the course come from the New Testament. This is not because the Old Testament is unimportant (far from it) but because most people know the New Testament better than the Old and, in a short course like this, will probably find it easier to reflect on passages they are more familiar with.

Making Good Sense of the Bible Together is a basic introduction to biblical interpretation, and seeks to whet your appetite for some big questions and issues. This is only the first step on a long journey. Making good sense of the Bible takes a lifetime's commitment – but it is an exciting journey and one that will take you deeper into the heart of God.

 Download a free Group Facilitators' Guide for guidance on leading the sessions from: **biblesociety.org.uk/mgsotb**

Session 1

Making Good Sense of the Bible: Why do we need to?

SESSION SUMMARY

This session explores some of the reasons why it is so important to make good sense of the Bible and looks at the key ways in which we go about making sense of things generally in our daily lives.

 Start out

Pray
Group facilitator, *you might like to open this session with the following prayer:*

> Teach me, LORD, the way of your decrees, that I may follow it to the end. Give me understanding, so that I may keep your law and obey it with all my heart. Direct me in the path of your commands, for there I find delight. Amen.
>
> (Prayer adapted from Psalm 119.33,34)

Discuss

As we begin this first session, discuss the following questions:

How do you feel about reading the Bible?

How often do you read it?

Which bits do you love and which do you find difficult?

In what ways has the Bible inspired or changed you (if it has)?

....

....

....

....

....

There are no wrong answers here – if you don't like it and don't read it, do say: it is important! The point of this is so that everyone in the group knows where you are coming from in the weeks that follow, so be honest. It will help.

Why do you think we need to make good sense of the Bible? What problems might be caused if we don't read the Bible well?

....

....

....

....

Read
Take a few minutes to read and reflect on the following comments on your own.

- One of the most important questions we face at the start of a course like this is why need to even ask the question about making good sense of the Bible. Surely we just open up the Bible, start reading and allow God to speak? Isn't a course like this in danger of fiddling with something that works perfectly well so that it breaks? Doesn't it run the risk of finding problems where there weren't any to start with?

- There is always a danger that biblical interpretation will spoil rather than enhance our reading of the Bible but there are some very good reasons why we should pay attention to making good sense of the Bible.

We need to make good sense of the Bible, so that we:

1. Avoid bad interpretations

- Some interpretations of the Bible have been responsible for bringing great evil into the world (e.g. interpretations which were used to support the Nazi party in 1930s Germany or apartheid in South Africa). Can you think of any other examples?

....

....

....

....

....

- Some interpretations are not wrong (in the sense of bringing evil into the world), rather they place unhelpful emphasis on themes or passages within the Bible (e.g. the view that believing in Christ will make you materially rich, sometimes called 'the prosperity Gospel'). Can you think of other examples?

....

....

....

....

- Some interpretations make a poor use of the Bible to support pre-established views or opinions (e.g. by just quoting verses at random from the Bible). Which opinions have you heard backed up by random verses lately? Why do you think this not a helpful or valid way of using the Bible?

....

....

....

....

....

2. Can become more like the people God wants us to be

It has often been said that reading the Bible well can help form Christian character – in other words it can help us to become more like the people that God wants us to be.

All scripture is inspired by God and is useful for teaching, for reproof, for correction, and for training in righteousness, [17] so that everyone who belongs to God may be proficient, equipped for every good work.

2 Timothy 3.16-17

3. **So that we can hear God speaking more clearly through his word**
Perhaps the most obvious reason why we need to make good sense of the Bible is because Christians believe that the Bible is the word of God and that when we read it thoughtfully and prayerfully God speaks. If this is the case then it makes sense to do our best to understand what it is saying as much as possible so that we can train our ears to hear God's voice more clearly.

Do you have any other thoughts about this section?

....

....

....

....

Take a few minutes to share your thoughts and reflections on this section as a group.

 # Explore

Group facilitator, *please read out the following section and lead the exercise below:*

The feeling of being a little bemused when reading the Bible is not new; even people in the Bible appeared to struggle to make sense of it. A well-known example of someone needing help to make good sense of the

Bible comes in **Acts 8** when a court official of the Ethiopian Queen, Candace, was reading the book of Isaiah:

> So Philip ran up to it [the chariot] and heard him reading the prophet Isaiah. He asked, "Do you understand what you are reading?" He replied, "How can I, unless someone guides me?" And he invited Philip to get in and sit beside him.
>
> Acts 8.30-31

Believe it or not, we spend the whole of our lives interpreting the world around us. It is just that most of the time we do it so quickly we don't even notice we have done it.

The problem we face when interpreting the Bible is that it comes from a world so far away from our own that our usual techniques of interpretation break down. This is one of the reasons why thinking about the principles of interpretation can help us to work out what we need to know in order to interpret the Bible well.

Exercise

For the next exercise you will need four different envelopes that have each contained a different type of post:

1. a piece of personal post (with a handwritten address)

2. a business letter with a typewritten address but no branding

3. a business letter with either typed address or see-through window and branding (e.g. electricity bill)

4. an item of junk mail.

Look at the envelopes and decide privately in what order you would open them and why. Share together the decisions you made. Did you all decide to open the letters in the same order or a different order? What factors on the envelope affected your decision?

Points to bear in mind:

- Could you tell where the letter came from? Did this tell you anything about who sent it?
- Did the handwriting/typewritten script affect your decision? Was there any branding on the envelope and did that affect when you thought you would open it?
- Would your own personal circumstances cause you to open the letters in a different order (e.g. if you were waiting for an important letter from the hospital)?

Notice

Group facilitator, please read out the following section:

As you will no doubt have gathered, the point of this exercise is that even when it comes to opening the post we make swift decisions based on:

- where the letter has come from
- what form the letter appears to take (i.e. what the envelope looks like)
- our own personal circumstances.

All of this affects how we relate to what we are looking at.

In biblical scholarship these three factors all play into arriving at our interpretation of a text. They are sometimes referred to as what is:

- **behind the text** – where the particular book or passage came from: who wrote it when and why
- **on or in the text** – what form the book or passage takes and what context it is in

- **in front of the text** – the issues and concerns that we bring to the text as readers.

Study

Group facilitator, *please ask someone in your group to read* **Luke chapter 15.**

As we explore the following questions, we are beginning to look at the author of Luke, the audience and context and how we might begin to make sense of this chapter for ourselves.

Discuss
As a group discuss the following questions:

Who was Jesus telling these stories to (Luke 15.1)?

How might each category of people have felt as he spoke, and who might they have related to in each parable?

How do the three stories relate to each other, and why do you think Luke chose to record them in this order?

What do you think Jesus is saying to you through these stories? How does it feel to hear about God's heart for the lost of this world?

....

....

....

....

....

 # Engage

What are the key things you will take away from this session?

....

....

....

....

....

....

....

....

As you come to the end of this first session, you might like to pray together.

Pray that the Holy Spirit will give you a love of the Bible, a willingness to do the work needed to read it well, and an openness to being transformed as you come to know God better through its pages.

Session 2

Making Good Sense of the World of the Author

Session summary

This session looks at the history that lies behind the text of the Bible and asks what difference it makes for us to understand the world of the author and what happens when scholars don't agree.

 Start out

Pray
Group facilitator, *you might like to open this session with the following prayer:*

> Give us knowledge and good judgement LORD, as we trust your commands and obey your word. You are good and what you do is good. Your word is more precious than silver and gold. Amen.
>
> (Prayer adapted from Psalm 119.66-72)

Discuss
As we begin this session, discuss the following questions:

> In the contemporary west, when people meet, their first question is often 'What do you do?' Why do you think this is? What can we learn about someone from their occupation and what might we miss?

....

....

....

Read
Group facilitator, *please read out the following section, then move to the discussion below.*

Knowing even a little about a person's background can help us to understand why they are as they are, why they react as they do and how they fit into the world.

People have always wanted to understand background. Read **Matthew 13.54–58** together:

> He came to his home town and began to teach the people in their synagogue, so that they were astounded and said, "Where did this man get this wisdom and these deeds of power? Is not this the carpenter's son? Is not his mother called Mary? And are not his brothers James and Joseph and Simon and Judas? And are not all his sisters with us? Where then did this man get all this?" And they took offence at him. But Jesus said to them, "Prophets are not without honour except in their own country and in their own house." And he did not do many deeds of power there, because of their unbelief.
>
> Matthew 13.54–58

Discuss

> This story connects the question of who Jesus was with his background. The people knew his family and where he came from but he surprised them by 'his wisdom' and deeds of power'. Why did they think they understood him because they knew who his family were?

....

....

Clearly their desire to know Jesus was both good and not so good – spend some time talking about what was good here about them wanting to 'know' who Jesus was, and what was less good.

 **E**xplore

Read
Group facilitator, *please ask someone in your group to read the following:*

A lot of the questions we need to ask to make good sense of the world of the author are questions we ask naturally anyway: who wrote this and why? When did they write it, and where were they?

The reason these questions are important to ask is that they help us to understand what was going on in the mind of the author and why they wanted to say what they said. This often involves reading between the lines. Making good sense of the world of the author can often require good detective skills.

Take for example these two passages from Paul's letter to the Philippians:

> **Philippians 1.12-14** I want you to know, beloved, that what has happened to me has actually helped to spread the gospel, so that it has become known

throughout the whole imperial guard and to everyone else that my imprisonment is for Christ; and most of the brothers and sisters, having been made confident in the Lord by my imprisonment, dare to speak the word with greater boldness and without fear.

Philippians 2.22–27 But Timothy's worth you know, how like a son with a father he has served with me in the work of the gospel. I hope therefore to send him as soon as I see how things go with me; and I trust in the Lord that I will also come soon. Still, I think it necessary to send to you Epaphroditus – my brother and co-worker and fellow soldier, your messenger and minister to my need; for he has been longing for all of you, and has been distressed because you heard that he was ill. He was indeed so ill that he nearly died. But God had mercy on him, and not only on him but on me also, so that I would not have one sorrow after another.

Discuss
As a group, discuss the following questions:

From what Paul says in verses 12–14, what do you think the Philippians' reaction was to Paul's imprisonment?

What can you tell from both passages about the relationship between Paul and the Philippians?

Again from both passages, what can you tell about the circumstances of his imprisonment? Who was guarding him? Could he have visitors?

Why do you think Paul sent Epaphroditus?

....

....

....

Read
Group facilitator, *please ask someone in the group to read the following:*

Simply reading between the lines can tell us a lot about what was going on behind a text, but it can't tell us everything. The next stage is to attempt to discover more about the historical circumstances that gave rise to the text. We know from the letter that Paul was in prison, but we don't know where. Knowing where he was would tell us when he wrote it.

- If he was in **Ephesus** when he wrote, the letter's date would be AD 53–55, in other words making it one of the earliest to be written.

- If he was in **Caesarea,** then the letter would have been written between AD 57–59, in other words in the middle of his ministry.

- If he wrote from **Rome,** then it was written between AD 59–61, in other words making it one of the last to be written.

If you are interested in knowing more about where Paul might have been when he wrote Philippians, the major arguments in favour and against the three locations can be found on page 59.

Discuss
For some people knowing when and where something was written makes a huge difference, for others it is of much less importance.

How important do you think it is?

What difference does it make to know/or not know when and where something was written?

....

....

....

....

 # **N**otice

Read
Take a few minutes to read and reflect on the
following section on your own.

Part of the skill of good biblical interpretation is
learning to ask really good questions of the passage
you are reading. As you will have noticed scholars
don't always give the same answers to the questions
but they often do begin with the same questions.

- What can I tell from the book or passage itself
  about the events that lie behind this text?

- What do I know about who wrote this book? When
  were they writing? Was there anything important
  going on then that might affect how they wrote?

- What might it have been like to live when this
  passage is set? What do I need to know about
  what is going on in this passage in order to be able
  to imagine what it might have been like?

When you have asked the questions you then need
to begin to look for some answers – commentaries
and handbooks to the Bible are a good place to begin
to look.

Do you have any other thoughts about this section?

....

....

....

....

....

....

Study

Group facilitator, *please ask someone in your group to read the following passage. We are going to try and understand something of the world of author as we explore this passage.*

Read Matthew 5.38-45

> "You have heard that it was said, 'An eye for an eye and a tooth for a tooth.' But I say to you, Do not resist an evildoer. But if anyone strikes you on the right cheek, turn the other also; and if anyone wants to sue you and take your coat, give your cloak as well; and if anyone forces you to go one mile, go also the second mile. Give to everyone who begs from you, and do not refuse anyone who wants to borrow from you. You have heard that it was said, 'You shall love your neighbour and hate your enemy.' But I say to you, Love your enemies and pray for those who persecute you, so that you may be children of your Father in heaven; for he makes his sun rise on the evil and on the good, and sends rain on the righteous and on the unrighteous."
>
> Matthew 5.38-45

It is widely accepted that this passage needs to be understood against a context of oppression and injustice.

At the time of Jesus, the Romans were an occupying army in Palestine. They were widely hated by the Jews because they imposed the '*Pax Romana*' or peace of Rome on all those they conquered and often used brutal, oppressive methods to ensure that the peace was kept.

The practice of Roman soldiers to force people to carry their pack for them is also well known*.

---

* "Jesus' ... example ... is drawn from the very enlightened practice of limiting the amount of forced labour that Roman soldiers could levy on subject peoples.

Mile markers were placed regularly beside the highways. A soldier could impress a civilian to carry his pack one mile only; to force the civilian to go farther carried with it severe penalties under military law. In this way Rome attempted to limit the anger of the occupied people and still keep its armies on the move. Nevertheless, this levy was a bitter reminder to the Jews that they were a subject people even in the Promised Land."

Walter Wink, *Jesus and Nonviolence: A Third Way*, p. 23

Discuss
As a group discuss the following questions:

> How might this passage be misinterpreted without understanding the cultural context?

> What light does any understanding of the political situation at the time of Jesus shed on this passage from Matthew?

> What does Jesus appear to be saying in the light of this Roman practice?

....

....

....

Engage

What have you learnt in this session (either from the course itself or your conversation with others) that you want to take away and think about more this week?

....

....

....

As you come to the end of this second session, you might like to pray together.

> Pray that God will give you a clear and sharp mind as you read the Bible, enabling you to hear what he wants to say to you and live the life in his kingdom he intended for you.

Session 3

Making Good Sense of the Text

Session summary

This session explores the text itself and asks how understanding the style of writing and the context in which the passage is set can help us to understand the passage.

 **S**tart out

Pray
Group facilitator, *you might like to open this session with the following prayer:*

> Your word, Lord, is eternal; it stands firm in the heavens. Your faithfulness continues through all generations; you established the earth and it endures. Help us as we study the Bible at a historical distance to know your enduring love for us.
>
> (Prayer adapted from Psalm 119.89–90)

Exercise
We begin this session by taking a look at
__John 1.1-14__ set out below

Both columns contain exactly the same translation but the left-hand one is set out as though it is prose and the right-hand one as though it is poetry.

John 1.1-14	John 1.1-14

In the beginning was the Word, and the Word was with God, and the Word was God. He was in the beginning with God. All things came into being through him, and without him not one thing came into being. What has come into being in him was life, and the life was the light of all people. The light shines in the darkness, and the darkness did not overcome it.
 	
  There was a man sent from God, whose name was John. He came as a witness to testify to the light, so that all might believe through him. He himself was not the light, but he came to testify to the light. The true light, which enlightens everyone, was coming into the world.
 	
  He was in the world, and the world came into being through him; yet the world did not know him. He came to what was his own, and his own people did not accept him. But to all who received him, who believed in his name, he gave power to become children of God, who were born, not of blood or of the will of the flesh or of the will of man, but of God.
	In the beginning was the Word,
	and the Word was with God,
	and the Word was God.
	He was in the beginning with God.
	All things came into being through him,
	and without him not one thing came into
	    being.
	What has come into being in him was life,
	and the life was the light of all people.
	The light shines in the darkness,
	and the darkness did not overcome it.
	
	There was a man sent from God,
	whose name was John.
	He came as a witness to testify to the
	    light,
	so that all might believe through him.
	He himself was not the light,
	but he came to testify to the light.
	The true light, which enlightens everyone,
	was coming into the world.
	
	He was in the world,
	and the world came into being through
	    him;
	yet the world did not know him.
	He came to what was his own,
	and his own people did not accept him.

And the Word became flesh and lived among us, and we have seen his glory, the glory as of a father's only son, full of grace and truth.	But to all who received him, who believed in his name, he gave power to become children of God, who were born, not of blood or of the will of the flesh or of the will of man, but of God. And the Word became flesh and lived among us, and we have seen his glory, the glory as of a father's only son, full of grace and truth.

Discuss

As a group discuss these questions:

Does it make a difference to see this passage laid out differently?

Do you read it the same or not?

The answer may be that it makes no difference at all. Feel free to say no if it makes no difference for you, but do say why you think that.

....

....

....

....

....

....

Read
Group facilitator, *please ask someone to read the following section to this group.*

One of the most important tips for reading the Bible well is to be alert to what kind of text (or genre) you are reading. The word genre simply refers to the style of text you have in front of you. In modern life, again we often make split-second decisions about genre without even noticing that we have done so, for example you read a telephone directory very differently than a novel; a take-away menu differently than a magazine article. Our brain sees what we are reading and seamlessly, often without us noticing, we read them differently to take their style into account.

The Bible is made up of a wide variety of different types and styles of writing and a first step towards reading them well is to recognise what type of writing they are and to try read them accordingly.

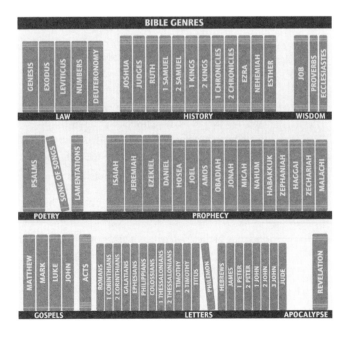

The books of the Bible fall into basic genres as the diagram illustrates, but there are also varieties within each book. So you will find a mix of poetry and prose, law and narrative, teaching and parable in different books.

 Explore

Read
Take a few minutes to read the following passages on your own.

> **Proverbs 19.11-12** Those with good sense are slow to anger, and it is their glory to overlook an offence. A king's anger is like the growling of a lion, but his favour is like dew on the grass.

> **Luke 13.20-21** And again he said, "To what should I compare the kingdom of God? It is like yeast that a woman took and mixed in with three measures of flour until all of it was leavened."

> **1 Thessalonians 1.1-3** Paul, Silvanus, and Timothy, To the church of the Thessalonians in God the Father and the Lord Jesus Christ: Grace to you and peace. We always give thanks to God for all of you and mention you in our prayers, constantly remembering before our God and Father your work of faith and labour of love and steadfastness of hope in our Lord Jesus Christ.

Discuss

Each one of these is a different genre of writing. Without trying to work out 'technical' names for the genres here (just working on what you know), what is the difference between these three, and do you read them differently?

....

....

....

....

Share your thoughts and reflections as a group.

Read
Now read the following section from:

> **Psalm 137.8-9** O daughter Babylon, you
> devastator! Happy shall they be who pay you back
> what you have done to us! Happy shall they be who
> take your little ones and dash them against the rock!

Discuss

Knowing that this is a piece of poetry, should you read it
any differently than if it were, for example, in Leviticus
and classed as law?

....

....

....

 # **N**otice

Group facilitator, *please read out the following
section to the group.*

Read
When you read a passage ask yourself:

- What genre or style of writing is this passage? Does it
  make a difference to how I should read what it says?

- What is the immediate context for this passage (bearing in mind that sometimes an immediate context can run to a few chapters). Does this affect how I read the text?

- What Old Testament references or allusions are there in this passage? How do these help me understand the passage better?

When you have asked the questions you then need to begin to look for some answers – handbooks to the Bible are often helpful for helping you work out genre questions. Another essential tool for understanding Old Testament references is a cross-reference Bible which will help you root out what passages may lie behind any given text.

In Christian worship we have developed the habit of reading the Bible in short chunks. In many ways this is a very good idea, not least because it avoids the need to sit there for hours on end while a whole book of the Bible is read out. There are, however, problems with reading the Bible like this. The biggest problem is that when we read the Bible regularly in short chunks it is easy to forget that it wasn't originally heard like that.

Another challenge for reading the New Testament is the fact that most New Testament writers appeared to assume that their readers knew their Old Testaments very well indeed. One of our problems is that often, because we do not know our Old Testaments as well as the New Testament writers think that we do, we miss some of the points that they were making.

 Study

Group facilitator, *please ask different people in the group to read the following passages, as we continue to make good sense of the text.*

Read

1 Peter 2.9-10 But you are a chosen race, a royal priesthood, a holy nation, God's own people, in order that you may proclaim the mighty acts of him who called you out of darkness into his marvellous light. Once you were not a people, but now you are God's people; once you had not received mercy, but now you have received mercy.

Isaiah 43.20-21 The wild animals will honour me, the jackals and the ostriches; for I give water in the wilderness, rivers in the desert, to give drink to my chosen people, the people whom I formed for myself so that they might declare my praise.

Exodus 19.6 "But you shall be for me a priestly kingdom* and a holy nation. These are the words that you shall speak to the Israelites."

Hosea 1.9 Then the LORD said, "Name him Lo-ammi, for you are not my people and I am not your God."

Hosea 1.6b Then the LORD said to him, "Name her Lo-ruhamah, for I will no longer have pity on the house of Israel or forgive them."

> * It might help you to know that the Hebrew of Exodus 19.6 says priestly kingdom but many Jews reading at the time of the early Church would have read the Greek translation of the Old Testament and there it was translated as royal priesthood.

Discuss
As a group, discuss the following questions.

What connections between 1 Peter 2.9-10 and these Old Testament passages can you find?

What points do you think Peter is making by using these texts?

Most scholars think that Peter was writing to Gentiles in 1 Peter. What is the significance of him using these passages which were originally addressed to the Israelites?

....

....

....

....

....

Engage

What have you learnt in this session (either from the course itself or your conversation with others) that you want to take away and think about more this week? What, if anything, will you do differently next time you read the Bible?

....

....

....

....

....

....

....

....

....

....

As you come to the end of this session, you might like to pray together.

Thank God for the beautiful diversity of literature in his Word. Pray for each other to grow in love and appreciation of this incredible book.

Making Good Sense of Translations

Session summary

This session looks at the question of translation, the principles that lie behind the translations we use to read the Bible and asks how this helps us to understand what we are reading better.

 **S**tart out

Pray
Group facilitator, *you might like to open this session with the following prayer:*

> Your righteousness is everlasting and your law is true. Your word is always righteous; give me understanding that I may live.
>
> (Prayer adapted from Psalm 119.142–144)

Discuss

As we begin this session, take a few minutes to read and reflect on the following:

When it comes to reading the Bible, English speakers are particularly fortunate since we have a huge range of translations of the Bible to choose from. This great gift can also cause problems, since the sheer range of available translations can be bewildering.

Spend some time in your group talking about whether you have a favourite translation of the Bible. Some people will, some people won't. Some will simply have chosen what everyone else has; others will have chosen one specifically. If you have a favourite translation, say why it is your favourite; if you don't have a favourite you might like to say what you would want in a Bible translation (accuracy, ease of reading, modern words, illustrations, poetry etc...).

 # Explore

Read

Take a few minutes to read this next section on your own and have a go at the exercise.

People often want advice about getting 'the best' translation but this advice can be hard to offer. What counts as 'the best' depends on what you want the translation for. For example, a new Christian might need a much more accessible translation whereas someone studying a passage in detail might want one as close to the original as possible.

Exercise

Read **Romans 12.1–2** as it is translated in the English Standard Version (ESV), which aims to be as accurate as possible, the Contemporary English Version (CEV) which aims to be as clear as possible, and the King

James Version (KJV) which aims to use language both poetically and accurately.

- Begin by noticing the differences between them. Do this phrase by phrase and see what you notice. Do any particular differences jump out at you?

- Discuss which of these translations you prefer. Is your preference down to personal taste or something else?

- From these verses, what do you think is lost by trying to be accurate and what is lost by trying to communicate well?

I appeal to you therefore, brothers, by the mercies of God, to present your bodies as a living sacrifice, holy and acceptable to God, which is your spiritual worship. Do not be conformed to this world, but be transformed by the renewal of your mind, that by testing you may discern what is the will of God, what is good and acceptable and perfect. **(ESV)**

Dear friends, God is good. So I beg you to offer your bodies to him as a living sacrifice, pure and pleasing. That's the most sensible way to serve God.
Don't be like the people of this world, but let God change the way you think. Then you will know how to do everything that is good and pleasing to him. **(CEV)**

I beseech you therefore, brethren, by the mercies of God, that ye present your bodies a living sacrifice, holy, acceptable unto God, which *is* your reasonable service. And be not conformed to this world: but be ye transformed by the renewing of your mind, that ye may prove what *is* that good, and acceptable, and perfect, will of God. **(KJV)**

....

....

....

....

....

....

....

....

Take a minute to share your thoughts and reactions with the group.

 **N**otice

Read
Group facilitator, *please read aloud the following section.*

Most people reading an English Bible will not be able to check their translation with the original language. It is often helpful to compare different translations to see what they do with a passage. You can do this easily these days as nearly all translations of the Bible are available on the internet for free. When reading a passage why not check to see what other translations say?

You might like to compare versions that come from a tradition other than your own – Catholic or Protestant, or a Jewish translation of the Old Testament for example. And if you use a very accessible version, you might like to compare it to a more word-for-word accurate version (and vice versa).

As you compare these versions, ask what is different between the translations. Is it important or not? Can you work out what the issues might be that have given rise to the difference?

When you have asked the questions, you then need to begin to look for some answers – in this instance commentaries will be your best help.

 **S**tudy

Read
Group facilitator, *please read the following section to the group and discuss the questions.*

Some of the time translation is relatively straight forward. At other times it is much harder to work out what the best translation should be. When translations are different from each other this is often a sign that the original is hard to put into English. In that case looking at the versions side by side can be illuminating!

Our first example of this is **John 2.4**. This is the well-loved story of the Wedding at Cana. After Mary said to Jesus that the wine had run out, Jesus responded to Mary literally in Greek: '*Woman, what to me and to you?*'

Translators have struggled to put this into English, below are some of the ways this has been translated

- And Jesus said to her, Woman, what have I to do with you? **(NASV)**

- And Jesus said to her, "Woman, what does this have to do with me?" **(ESV)**

- "Woman, why do you involve me?" Jesus replied **(NIV)**

- Jesus said, 'Woman, what do you want from me?' **(NJB)**

- Jesus said to her, "Woman, what does your concern have to do with me? "**(NKJV)**

- "Dear woman, that's not our problem," Jesus replied. **(NLT)**

- And Jesus said to her, "Woman, what concern is that to you and to me?" **(NRSV)**

Discuss

What do you think are the issues that the translations are struggling with here?

Which translation of this verse do you prefer and why?

Do you get a better sense of the verse by looking at all the different versions or do you just find the range confusing?

....

....

....

....

....

Read

A second example comes from Paul.

One of Paul's most iconic and important verses is **2 Corinthians 5.17**. Literally the Greek for this verse says '*If anyone in Christ new creation.*' Obviously it is impossible to leave the English like that so extra words need to be inserted in order to make it make sense. The question is which words?

Compare the ESV translation of this verse with the 2011 NIV:

- Therefore, if anyone is in Christ, he is a new creation. The old has passed away; behold, the new has come. **(ESV)**

- Therefore, if anyone is in Christ, the new creation has come: the old has gone, the new is here! **(NIV)**

Discuss

What is the difference between what these versions are saying?

Is one better than another? Or do you get a fuller picture of what Paul is saying here with both together?

....

....

....

....

....

....

....

Engage

What have you learnt in this session (either from the course itself or your conversation with others) that you want to take away and think about more this week? Is there anything you want to do differently next time you read a biblical passage?

....

....

....

....

....

As you come to the end of this session, you might like to pray together:

> Thank God that we can read the Bible in our own language, and for the work of translators through the years. Pray for those working to translate the Bible into new languages, and for the ongoing work on our English versions.

Making Good Sense of the Reader

Session summary

This session thinks about ourselves as we come to the text and the importance of understanding the lenses through which we read the Bible.

 ## Start out

Pray
Group facilitator, *you might like to open this session with the following prayer.*

> You are our refuge and our shield, and we have put our hope in your word. Sustain us according to your promise. Make your face shine on us, and show us more of who you are. Amen.
>
> (Prayer adapted from Psalm 119.114, 116, 135)

Read
***Group facilitator**, please read the following
section to the group and discuss the question at
the end.*

Think back to the very first session with the envelopes
that you looked at. One of the factors that affects
how important we think a letter is, is our own
circumstances. If, for example, we are awaiting a letter
from a doctor, we might fall on a very formal looking
letter much more quickly than we would otherwise.

   Inevitably who we are and what is happening in our
lives affects how we respond to a passage. The key is to
be aware of this and to notice how it impacts our reading.

Discuss

> Think of a time when a particular bit of the Bible was
> significant to you. What passage was it and how did it
> speak to what was going on? How might someone else,
> in different circumstances, have read its message?

....

....

....

....

....

 # Explore

Read
*Take a few minutes to read and reflect on the
following section on your own.*

A scholar from the USA asked 100 American students
at a Bible college to retell the story of the prodigal son

(Luke 15.11–32). He noticed that all but six of them told the opening of the story in the same way.

- A young man acquired his inheritance prematurely.

- He squandered his property in a faraway land.

- He was left in dire straits.

What only 6% of the **Americans** included was that after he squandered his property there was a famine in the land. In other words the American students blamed his lack of food on his squandering of his own resources.

He then did a similar exercise with a group of **Russian** readers. In great contrast 84% of the Russians noted the famine, while only 34% of them mentioned that the son had squandered his wealth. In their view he was hungry primarily because of the famine. His sin was leaving home, not squandering the money.

Finally he asked a group of **Tanzanian** readers about the story and asked them why the son was hungry. 80% of them said it was because no one had given him anything to eat. He was in a faraway country where it is easy to lose your money and someone should have looked after him.

In short the American audience thought it was his fault; the Russian audience that it was no one's fault, but due to natural disaster; the Tanzanian audience thought it was due to lack of care from the people in the land he had gone to.

Taken from Mark Allan Powell *What Do They Hear?: Bridging the Gap Between Pulpit and Pew* (Abingdon Press, 2007), chapter 2 Social Location

Discuss

Do you think any of these readings are wrong?

Do any of them strike you as more correct than the others?

Why do you think such overwhelming majorities in the different groups saw and heard such different things in the passage?

What can we learn from this about how we interpret the Bible?

....

....

....

....

....

....

....

....

Share your thoughts as a group.

 # Notice

Read
Split into twos or threes, and read **Mark 14.1-9.** Then close your Bibles and retell the story to each other, remembering as many details as you can. Go back to the text and see which details you forgot, or anything that is not how you remembered. Feed back what happened to the whole group.

When you read a passage ask yourself:

- What details about this passage have jumped out at me? Is there anything about who I am or what is happening to me at the moment that has drawn them to my eye?

Look at the text again (Mark 14.1-9). Try to imagine what it might be like if you were a different gender, had a different marital status, or were experiencing different circumstances. What might you see if you were someone different?

When you have asked the questions you might want to try harder to imagine how different people might read the text. You could look for interpretations from different cultures or traditions to see if this sheds any different light on what you were reading.

 # Study

Read

As someone reads out the following passage, try to imagine what the scene looked like. Can you see Jesus' face? What does it feel like to be there? Do you sympathise more with one character than another?

Read Mark 5.22-43

Discuss

Is there anything about you that made you associate more with one character than another?

Did being male or female affect how you felt?

Maybe being a parent or not being a parent made a difference?

Have you ever been very ill? Did this make a difference?

Did you notice anything else that affected how you felt about the story?
(Only share what you feel comfortable with here.)

....

....

....

....

....

....

Engage

What are the key things you will take away from this session?

....

....

....

....

....

....

As you come to the end of this session, you might like to pray together.

Pray that God will give you insight into what you bring to the reading of the Bible, so that you can be aware of ways you might be skewing what you hear.

SESSION 6

Making Good Sense of Ourselves: How can the Bible help?

Session summary

This session turns full circle and asks how it is that making good sense of the Bible actually helps us to make good sense of ourselves.

 Start out

Pray
Group facilitator, *you might like to open this session with the following prayer:*

> We long for your salvation, LORD, and your laws give us delight. Let us live that we may praise you, and may your laws sustain us. Amen.
>
> (Prayer adapted from Psalm 119.174,5)

Read

Group facilitator, *please read the following section to the group.*

When we read the Bible carefully – paying close attention to how it reached the form that it did, what styles it adopts, what difference context makes, how it is translated and what we bring to the text – then we discover that it changes us. We don't so much read the Bible, as the Bible reads us.

Discuss

Psalm 1.3 says that those who meditate on the law of the Lord become like trees planted by streams of water which produce fruit at the right time.

What do you think the psalmist meant by this image? How does he imagine that we are influenced by the Bible?

Can you think of any other images from the Bible that describe how the Bible changes us and our lives?

....

....

....

....

....

....

....

....

 **E**xplore

Take a few minutes to look at the diagram, read the section below and reflect on the questions on your own.

Read

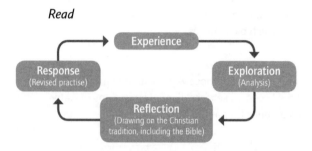

The Christian growth cycle suggests that the way we grow as people generally but also as Christians is through a four-fold movement:

- we explore the text

- we reflect on the text using the questions raised in this course and drawing on Christian tradition and teaching

- we respond differently in what we do

- our experience changes

- (and on the cycle goes).

In other words, we cannot remain the same if we are reading the Bible as well as we can. The more we read it with reflection, practice and experience, the more we turn into the people God yearns for us to become.

If you were going to read the Bible using this cycle of exploration, reflection, response and experience, what would you would need to change about how you read the Bible at the moment?

Can you see any pitfalls in this kind of method that you might want to be careful about? How might you avoid these pitfalls?

Where might your church community fit into this cycle?

Where might the Holy Spirit fit into this cycle?

....

....

....

....

....

....

....

....

....

....

....

....

....

Take a few minutes to share your thoughts and reflections on this section as a group.

 # Notice

Read
Group facilitator, *please read the following section to the group.*

Tom Wright, the New Testament scholar and former Bishop of Durham, talks about good reading of the Bible being like the performance of a five-act play. If you would like to read his extended theory for yourself, he most recently laid it out in his book *Scripture and the Authority of God: How to Read the Bible Today* (SPCK, 2013).

He sees the story of redemption as being like a five-act play, with much of the act five missing. The play is so important that actors want to put on the play despite the loss of a portion of the final act. In order to do so they treat the text as authoritative, so authoritative in fact, that they remain in character as actors as they improvise the final scenes. Tom Wright argues that this is the church's vocation. It has the first four acts and a bit of the fifth (creation, fall, Israel, Jesus and the start of the early church) but the rest of the story must be improvised by us as Christians.

He says,

> We read Scripture in order to be refreshed in our memory and understanding of the story within which we ourselves are actors, to be reminded where it has come from and where it is going to, and hence what our own part within it ought to be.
>
> *Scripture and the Authority of God: How to Read the Bible Today*, (SPCK, 2013, p. 116).

As a result we do not read Scripture simply as interested bystanders but as actors in a play who need to know how to improvise our part in that play and a way that stays faithful to what has come before.

Discuss

How might thinking about the Bible like this change the way in which you read it?

How might it change the way you live your life?

Is there anything unhelpful or troubling to you about the idea?

....

....

....

....

....

Read

When you read a passage ask yourself:

- Have I read this passage before?

- If yes, can I remember what I thought about it when I last read it?

- Using the tools learnt in this course and elsewhere, explore the passage in detail, then ask:

  > What from this passage requires further reflection?

  > What might this passage be asking me to doing differently?

  > How will this passage change me to be more who God wants me to be?

  > What might the Church be called to be and do as it improvises the last act of this story of salvation?

 **S**tudy

Group facilitator, *please ask someone in your group to read the following section out loud and then discuss the questions below.*

Read Acts 10.1-16

Read

Sometimes when we read the Bible we need to be changed in order to see it properly. An interesting example of this was what happened to Peter in **Acts 10**.

The story goes on from here to describe Peter's visit to Cornelius' house and his acceptance that now Cornelius, a gentile, could be welcomed by God. This passage ends with Peter's declaration that reads like this:

> Then Peter began to speak to them: "I truly understand that God shows no partiality, but in every nation anyone who fears him and does what is right is acceptable to him. You know the message he sent to the people of Israel, preaching peace by Jesus Christ – he is Lord of all. That message spread throughout Judea, beginning in Galilee after the baptism that John announced.
>
> Acts 10.34-37

It is clear that Peter's 'lens' changed during the course of this story and at the end he saw things differently. We need to be clear that Peter's lens at the start of this passage was not wrong. He was a devout Jew and was doing what Scripture told him to, but his experience of God and his vision changed his perspective so that he welcomed Cornelius in a way he could not have done before.

Discuss

Why did Peter's lens need to change? What was it that changed his lens?

When he went back to the Scriptures that forbade him to eat non-kosher meat and to mix with gentiles, how do you think he read those passages after this experience?

....

....

....

....

....

 # Engage

Some might say that we do not need any of the techniques that we have explored throughout this course because it is the Spirit that helps us to read the Bible anyway.

It is true that Scripture is inspired at all stages by the Holy Spirit – including when we read it. The apostle Paul was very clear, however, that using our minds and being open to the Spirit are not mutually exclusive but are complementary:

> What should I do then? I will pray with the spirit, but I will pray with the mind also; I will sing praise with the spirit, but I will sing praise with the mind also.
>
> 1 Corinthians 14.15

Discuss

How might you develop a practice of Bible reading that blends together openess to the spirit while using your mind and techniques you've explored in this session?

As you come to the end of this course what are the main things you will take away with you?

....

....

....

....

....

....

....

....

As you come to the end of this session you might like to pray together.

Pray that as you read the Bible, God's Spirit would bring it alive to you.

More information for Session 2

If you are interested in the question of where Paul was in prison, the arguments for the different locations are laid out below.

You might think that it would be quite easy to work out where Paul was when he wrote this letter but scholars would not agree. Below are the pros and cons for each location:

- The traditional location for the letter is **Rome**.

  > Pros: we know he was in prison there, it makes sense of Paul being guarded by the imperial guard (i.e. the emperor's soldiers - though it is worth noting that it is possible to explain the soldiers' presence in both Ephesus and Caesarea. It is just more likely that they would be in Rome).

  > Cons: Rome is a long way from Philippi and it is not clear whether there would have been enough time for the Philippians to learn that Paul was in prison, to send Epaphroditus to help him, to have learned that Epaphroditus was ill and for Paul to have written Philippians in that space of time. Also important is the issue of Paul's determination to visit the Philippians again. If he were in prison in Rome

towards the end of his ministry, it raises the question of whether he could plan to see them again. Another issue that some think is a problem is that this puts Paul's imprisonment about ten years after Paul first visited. Some wonder whether Paul's relationship with the Philippians would have stayed so close over this time.

- Many people suggest **Ephesus**.

  > Pros: it is much closer to Philippi and would have made regular visits easier. Both this location and Caesarea would mean that it was also closer in time to Paul's founding of the church in Philippi. Since we know that the Philippian church helped Paul financially at the start of his ministry (Philippians 4.15-16) it makes sense of them sending him a gift in prison, if this were early in his ministry. It also makes sense of his optimism about what he would do when he left prison (an optimism which might be more difficult to explain if he were in Rome).

  > Cons: there is no record of Paul being in prison in Ephesus and it is not obvious why he would have been guarded by the imperial guard in that location. Many also suggest **Caeserea.**

  > Pros: we know Paul was in prison there and the imperial guard could have been attached to Herod's palace.

  > Cons: like Rome, it was a long way from Philippi.

More information for Session 4

Translation from any one language into another language has two main goals:

- to be as close as you can be in the new language to what was originally said in the old language

- to put across the ideas of what was said in a way that makes sense in the new language.

Within biblical translation these two goals have the technical names of:

- formal equivalence (a word-for-word translation of the original Hebrew or Greek)

- dynamic equivalence (a sense-for-sense translation, aiming to have the same effect on the reader as the original would have had).

In other words, formal equivalence aims to be as close to the Hebrew or Greek as possible whereas dynamic equivalence tries to communicate what is being said as clearly as possible. Dynamic equivalence translations of the Bible begin from the original language (Hebrew or Greek), while paraphrases start from another English translation and try to make it easier to understand. These are out of fashion these days and the only true paraphrase around is the Living Bible.

All translations make a decision in principle about where they want to place their emphasis (more on accuracy or more on comprehension).

Other decisions also lie behind translations, for example, some choose to use gender inclusive language (e.g. NRSV and the most recent NIV); some come from the Catholic church (e.g. the Jerusalem and New Jerusalem Bible); some try to be easier to read in public (KJV or the Revised English Bible).

If you would like to read more about this, see chapter 4 of Paula Gooder's *The Bible: A Beginners' Guide* (Oneworld, 2013) which discusses translation theory in more depth.

Translations that seek to be close to the original language	Translations that seek a mid-point between accuracy and communication	Translations that seek to be easy to read	Paraphrases
King James Version (KJV)	NIV	CEV	The Living Bible
Revised Standard Version (RSV)		The Message	
New Revised Standard Version (NRSV)		Good News Bible	
English Standard Version (ESV)			
New American Standard Bible (NASB)			

Want to read more?

You may find these books helpful:

Richard Briggs *Light to Live By: How to Interpret the Bible* (Scripture Union, 2005).

Gordon D Fee and Douglas Stuart *How to Read the Bible for All its Worth* (Zondervan, 2003).

Paula Gooder *The Bible: A Beginners' Guide* (Oneworld, 2013).

Mark Allan Powell *What Do They Hear?: Bridging the Gap Between Pulpit and Pew* (Abingdon Press, 2007).

Tom Wright *Scripture and the Authority of God: How to Read the Bible Today* (SPCK, 2013).

BIBLE SOCIETY